The Dragon and the Gold

by PATTY WOLCOTT
pictures by EMILY ARNOLD McCULLY

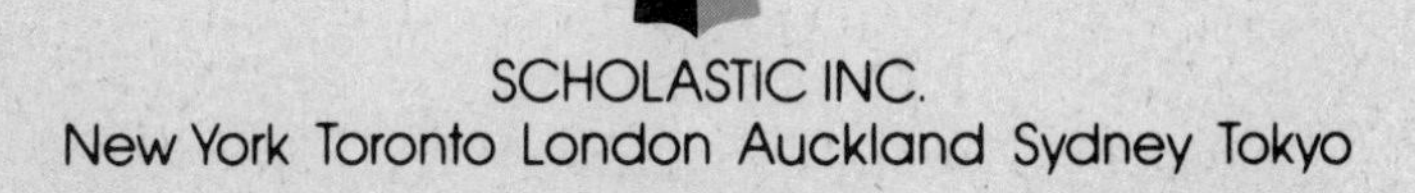

SCHOLASTIC INC.
New York Toronto London Auckland Sydney Tokyo

ISBN 0-590-32469-1

12 11 10 9 8 7 6 5 4 3 2 1 11 3 4 5 6 7/8

Printed in the U.S.A. 07

Gold! Gold!
I love gold!
1, 2, 3, 4, 5...
ROYAL CASTLE.

6, 7, 8,
9, 10...
ROYAL CASTLE
CANDY

?
11, 12, 13...

14, 15, 16...
Gold! I love gold!

The prince! I'll capture the prince!

A ransom note.

A ransom note.
RANSOM NOTE
Of CANDY

Ooooo!
ROYAL CASTLE
?
?

ROYAL CASTLE
Dragon! Dragon!
A ransom note?

Ha! Ha!
The dragon captured the prince!
The prince! The prince!
CANDY
RANSOM NOTE

A ransom note:
"Give me the gold
and I'll give you
the prince."
The Dragon.
CANDY

I'll capture the dragon
and rescue the prince.
You?
You?
You?

CANDY

CANDY

CLOSED

I will capture the dragon. I will capture the dragon and rescue the prince.

DRAGON CAVE
Gold, gold, gold.
I love gold.

Gold, gold, gold,
I love gold.
Gold I love.
Gold, gold, gold.

Dragon, Dragon! Give me the prince!
Give you the prince? You? Ha! Ha! Ha!

Give me the prince and I'll give you gold.
Gold?

You give **me** the gold and I'll give you the prince!

Gold! Gold!

?
I'll capture the dragon and the dragon's gold.

Candy!

I love
candy.

I love candy.

I love candy.

I feel
sick.

Ooooooo!
I feel sick.

I feel sick,
sick, sick.

You and I
will capture
the dragon.

?
The dragon is captured.

The gold is captured.

Prince! Prince!
Prince!
ROYAL CASTLE
The
prince

Is the dragon captured?
The dragon is captured!
CASTLE
Prince! Prince!
You captured the dragon?
The dragon!
The prince!
The prince and the dragon!

Give me the dragon, and I'll give you gold.
I'll give you the dragon, and you give me the prince.

I'll give you the prince.
I'll give you gold.
I'll give the prince gold.

Prince!
I love you.

For everybody?
Here is the dragon's gold for everybody!
For everybody!
For me?

And here is my gold for everybody!
For me?
For everybody!

I love you.
I love you.

ROYAL MENAGERIE
Goldie the Dragon